# What Does the X-Ray Say?

**Written and Illustrated by Second Grade Students of
Longfellow Elementary in West Allis, Wisconsin**

Scholastic Inc.
New York  Toronto  London  Auckland  Sydney  Mexico City  New Delhi  Hong Kong  Buenos Aires

ORIGINAL COVER

WE WOULD LIKE TO DEDICATE THIS BOOK

TO OUR MOMS

TO OUR DADS

One day, Rayann sat in the hospital with a sore neck waiting for the doctor to give her a check.

Jumping on her parents' bed

was a big

mistake.

Now she had a pain
that ached and ached.

The doctor said she needed an x-ray to see what happened inside her that day.

A huge machine
starting clicking away.
Rayann was
worried
what the
x-ray
would say.

The doctor thought
she should not be
left alone.

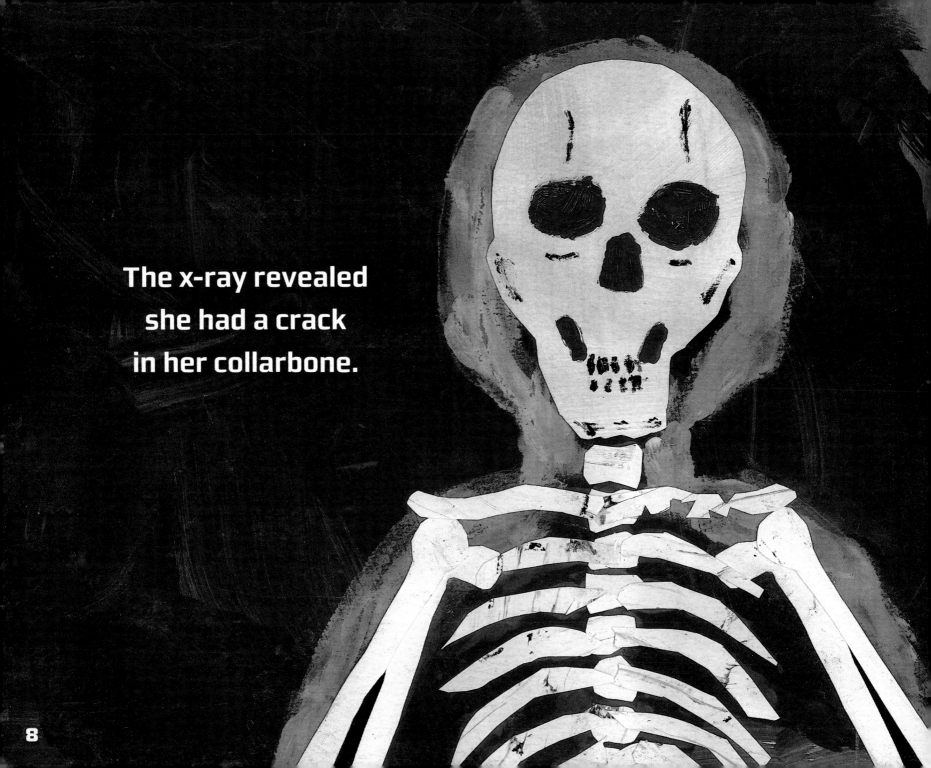

The x-ray revealed
she had a crack
in her collarbone.

Rayann needed rest,
as well as a sling.
X-rays sometimes
show
the weirdest things!

X-rays reveal some interesting sights.
Let's take a look at some blacks and whites.

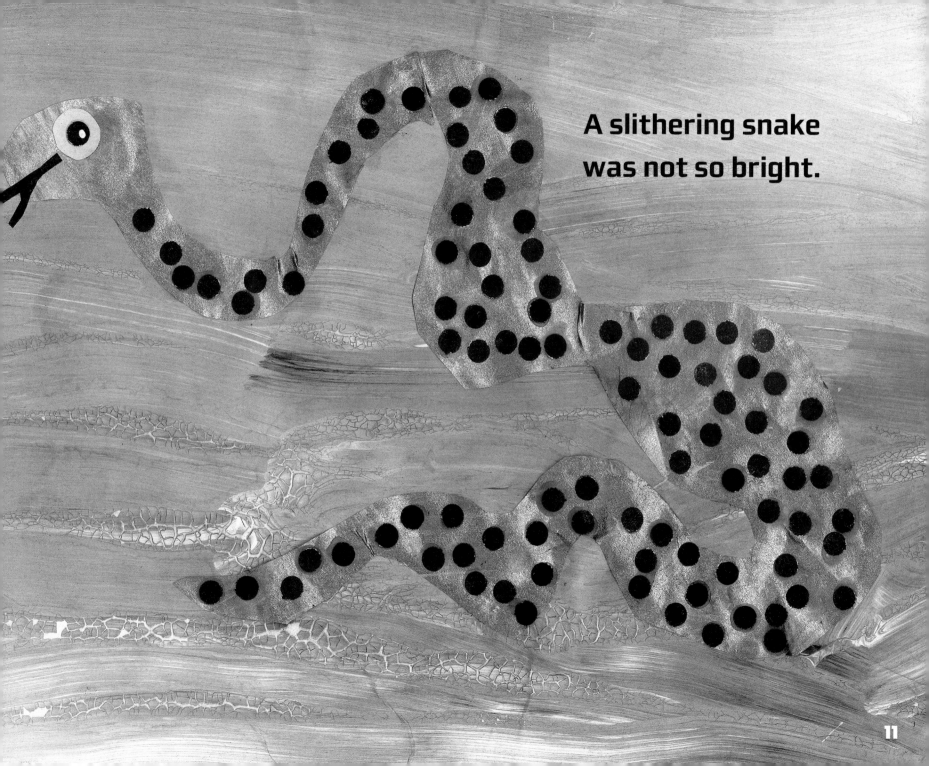

A slithering snake
was not so bright.

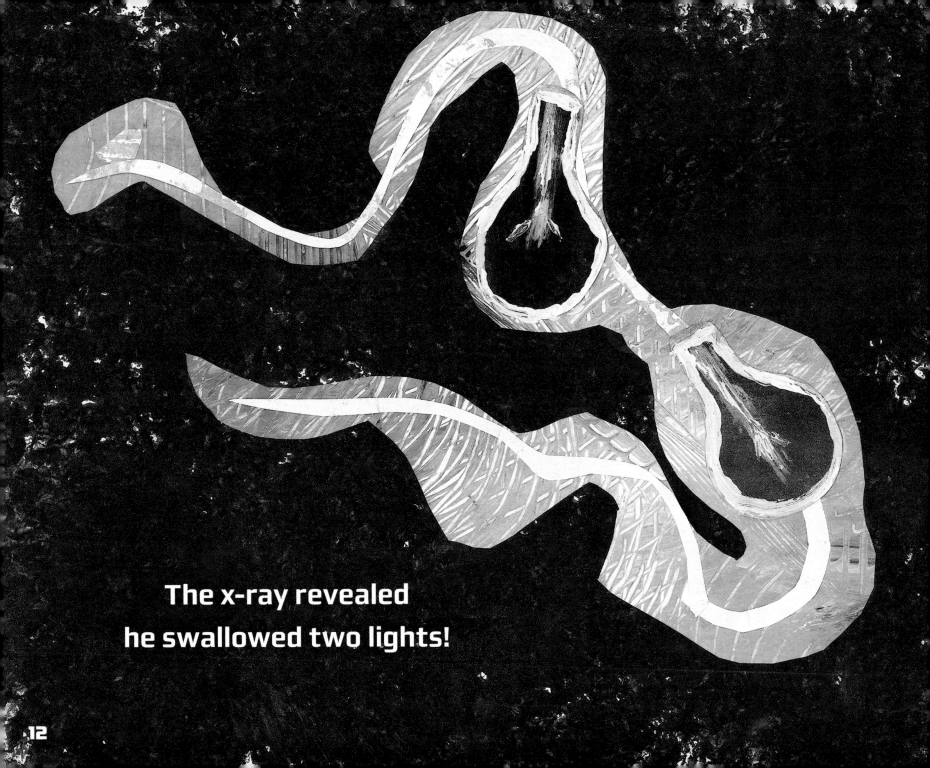

The x-ray revealed
he swallowed two lights!

A hungry
turtle should
have taken
a second look.

13

The x-ray
revealed
he swallowed
a fish hook!

This kid better be careful next time.

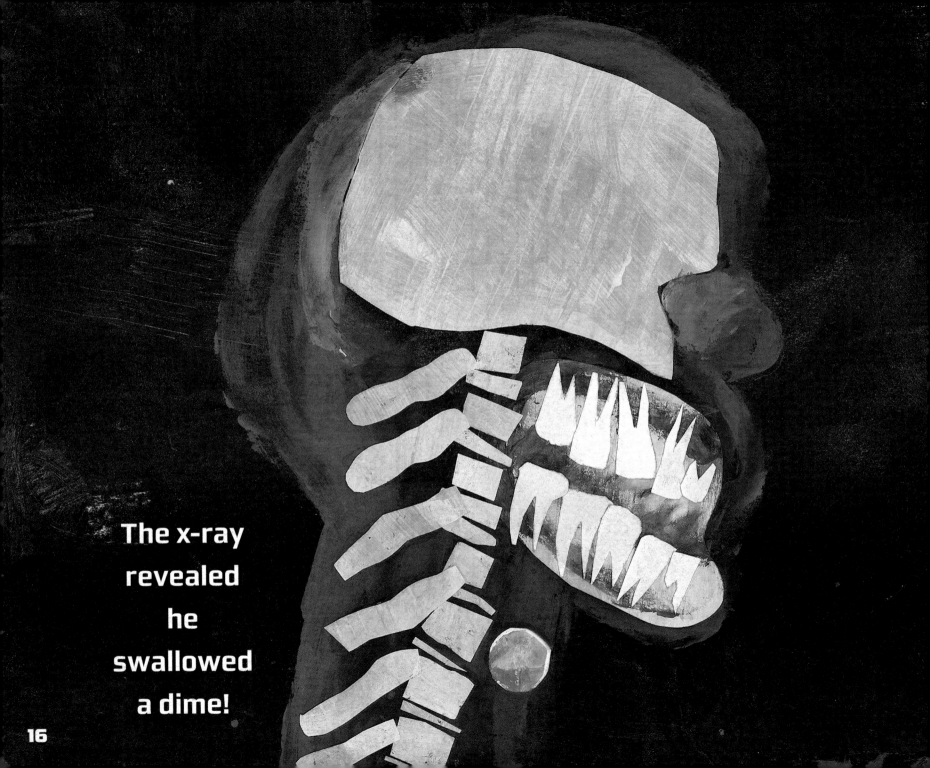

The x-ray
revealed
he
swallowed
a dime!

This poor dog was
out of luck.

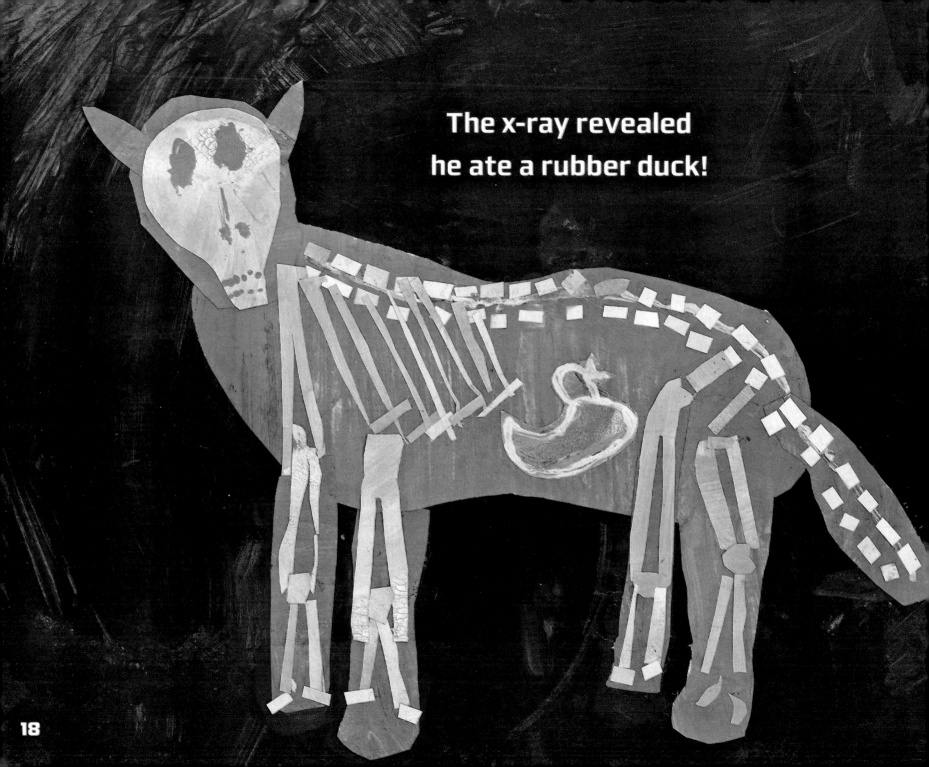

The x-ray revealed
he ate a rubber duck!

A woman was running
and fell in the sand.

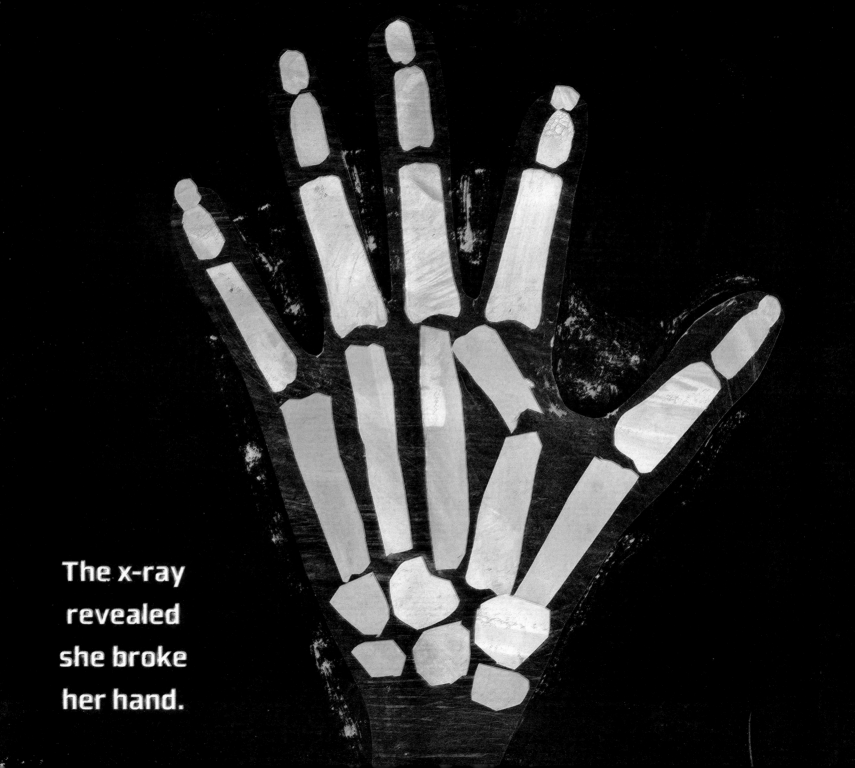

The x-ray
revealed
she broke
her hand.

This cat owner had a strange story to tell.

Maybe getting married just wasn't his thing.

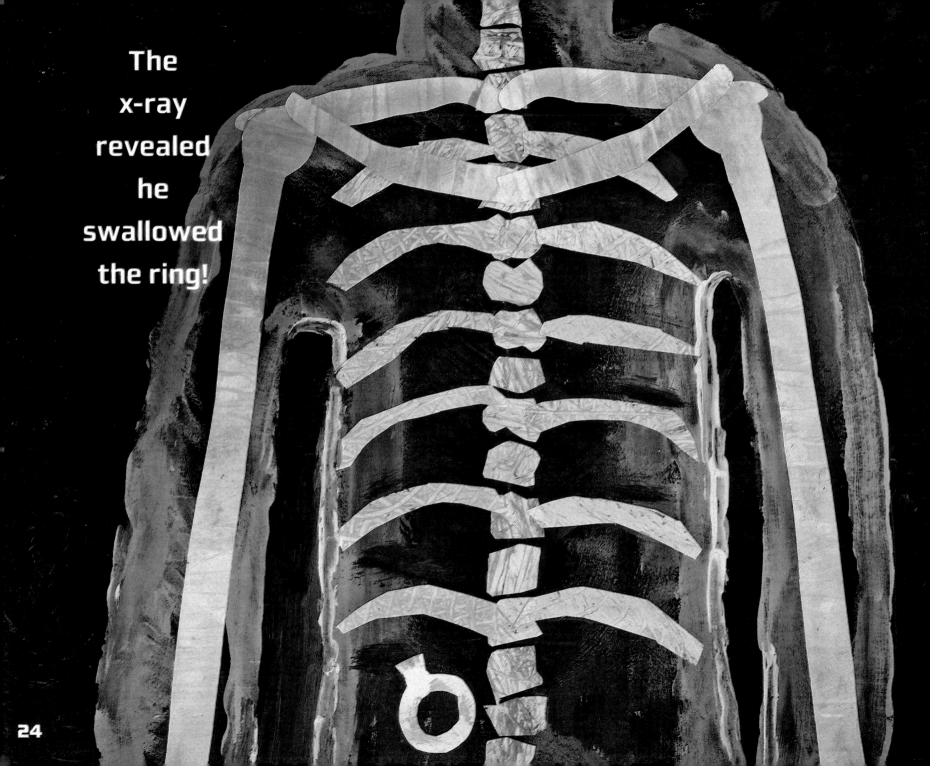

The
x-ray
revealed
he
swallowed
the ring!

This hungry dog's vet got lots of calls.

The x-ray
revealed he
swallowed 33 golf balls!

And so the X-ray
is the only way
you can be sure
the doctor finds a cure
for an ache
or a break.

# MEET THE AUTHORS

David Gonzalez

Mrs. Wandsneider

Michael Owen

Emily Stabb

Claudia Garcia

Mark Balcerowski

Isaac Dewaal

Hannah Caswell

Elizabeth Stabb

Lindsi Jensen

Victor Jose

Rayann Klitzka

Carlos Reyes

Susie Bethe

Dominic Ornelas

Alexia Senger

Juliana Perez-Colon

Mariah Rivera

**Kids Are Authors®**

Books written by children for children

The Kids Are Authors® Competition was established in 1986 to encourage children to read and to become involved
in the creative process of writing.

Since then, thousands of children have written and illustrated books as participants in the Kids Are Authors® Competition.

The winning books in the annual competition are published by Scholastic Inc.
and are distributed by Scholastic Book Fairs throughout the United States.

For more information:

Kids Are Authors® 1080 Greenwood Blvd.; Lake Mary, FL 32746 or visit our web site at: www.scholastic.com/kidsareauthors

ISBN 13: 978-0-545-40291-0     12 11 10 9 8 7 6 5 4 3 2 1

Cover design by Bill Henderson

Printed and bound in the U.S.A.     First Printing, July 2011